Air show

Apple trees

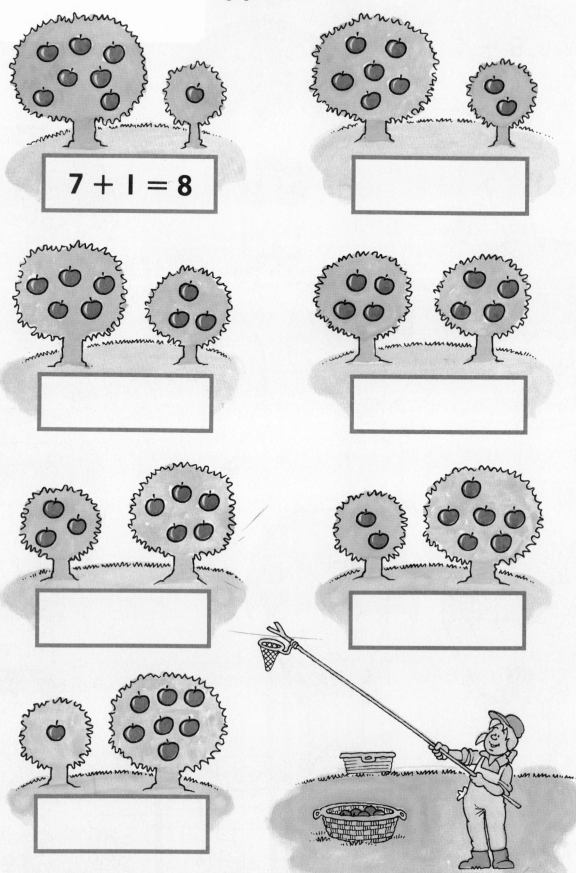

7 + 1 = 8

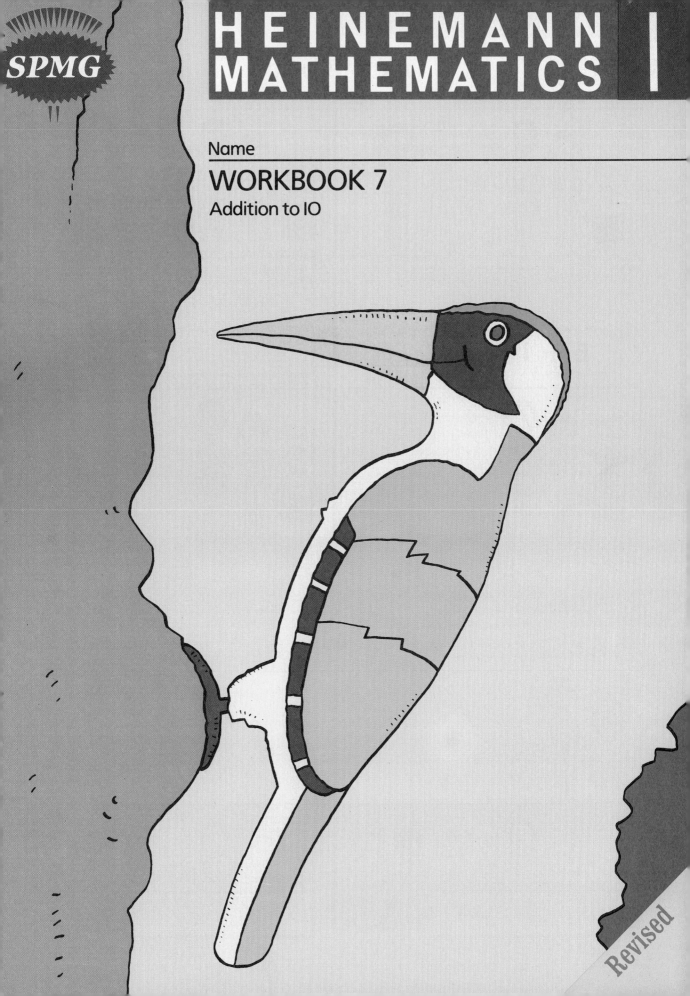

SPMG

HEINEMANN MATHEMATICS 1

Name

WORKBOOK 7
Addition to 10

Revised

1

At the pool

6 + 1 = 7

Apples

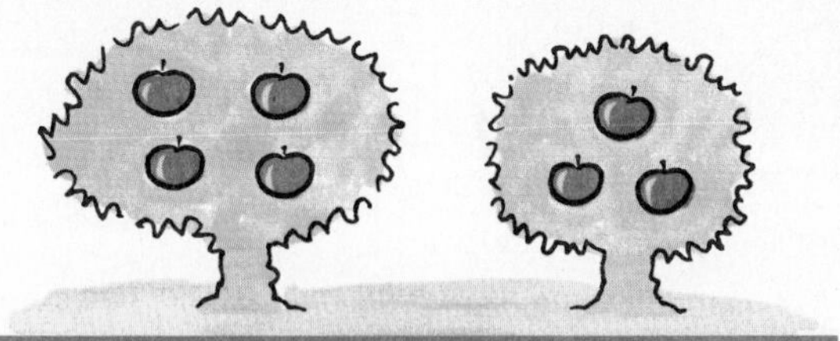

4 + 3 =

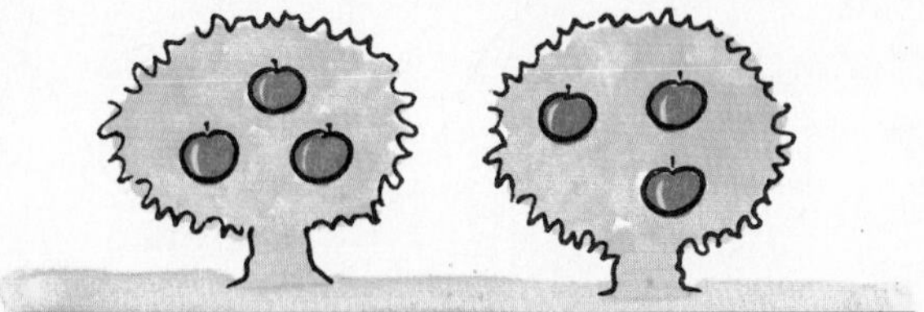

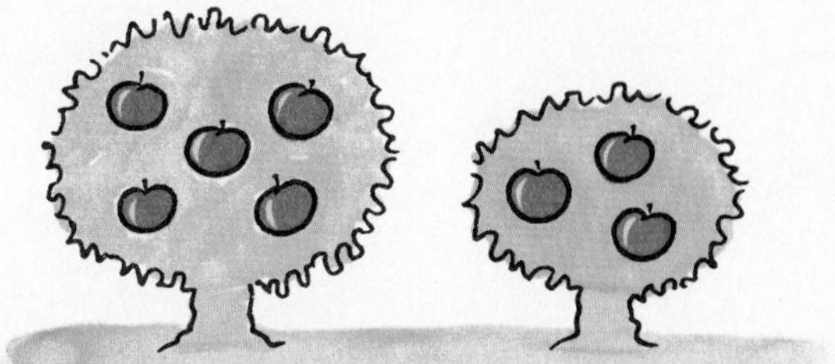

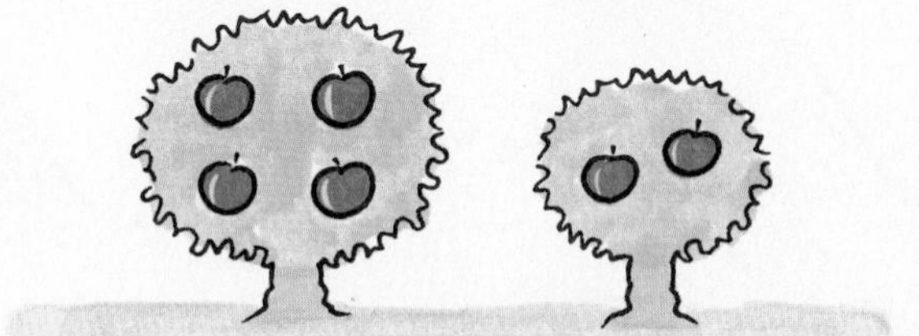

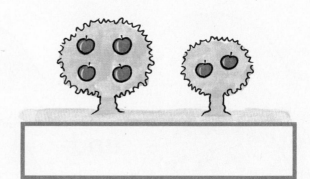

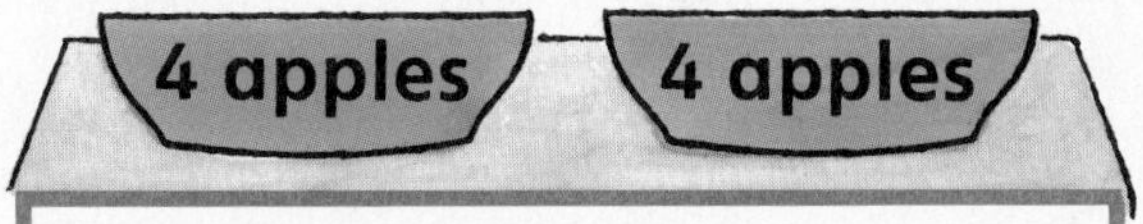
4 apples
4 apples

4 + 4 =

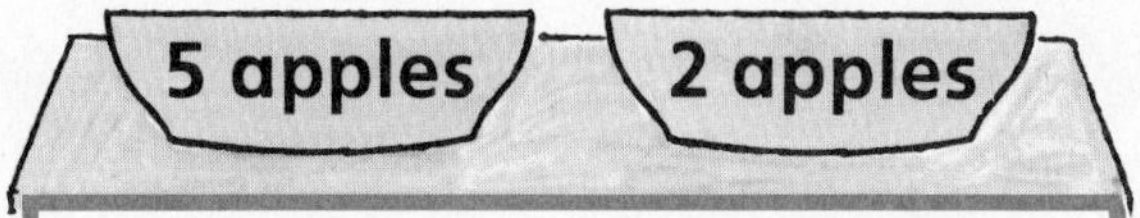
5 apples
2 apples

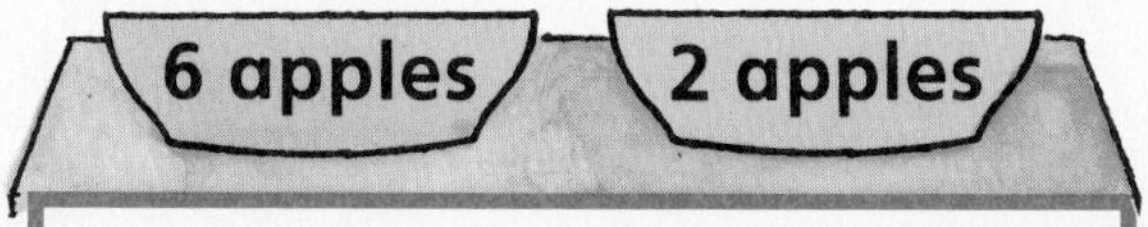
6 apples
2 apples

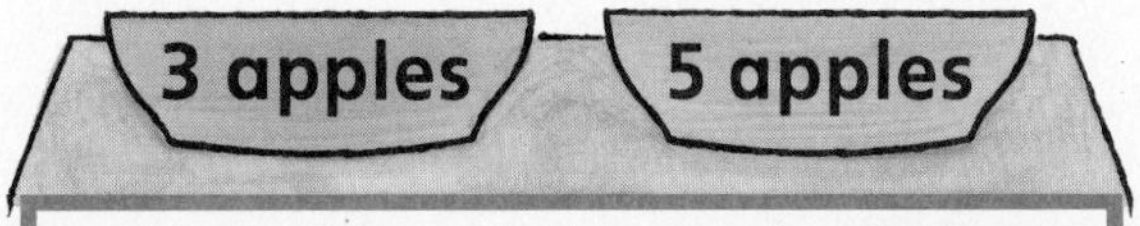
3 apples
5 apples

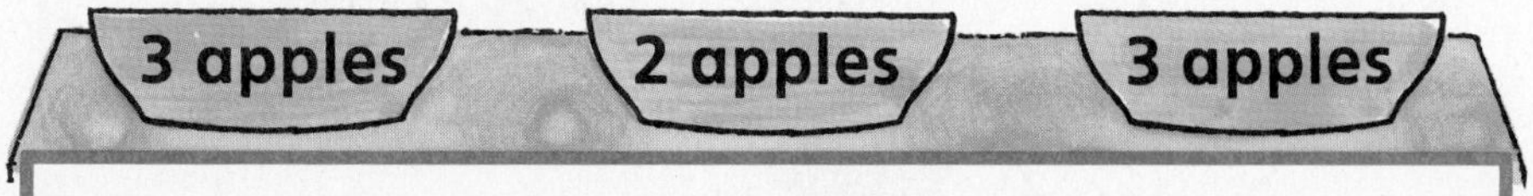
3 apples
2 apples
3 apples

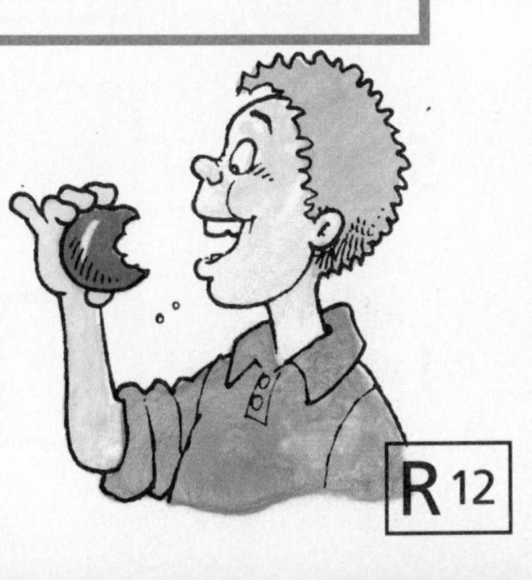

Ant hills

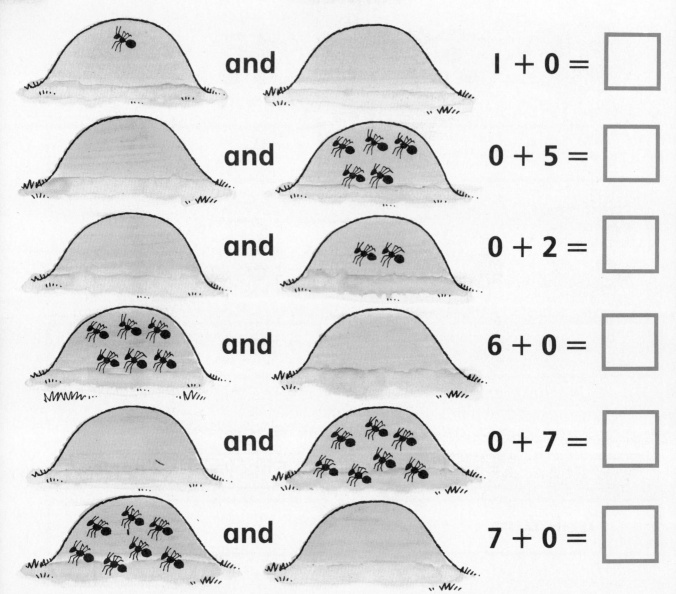

and   1 + 0 = ☐

and   0 + 5 = ☐

and   0 + 2 = ☐

and   6 + 0 = ☐

and   0 + 7 = ☐

and   7 + 0 = ☐

0 + 6 = ☐   8 + 0 = ☐   3 + 0 = ☐

5 + 0 = ☐   0 + 8 = ☐

1 + 7 = ☐   4 + 0 = ☐

Peas

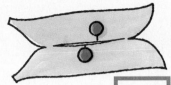

1 + 1 =

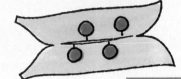

2 + 2 =

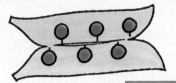

3 + 3 =

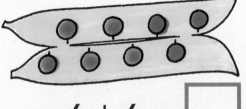

4 + 4 =

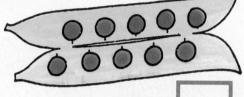

5 + 5 =

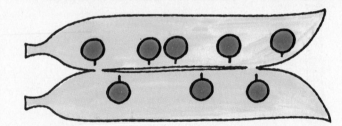

5 + 3 =

3 + 5 =

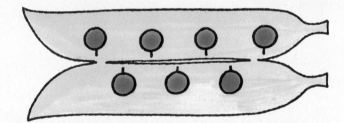

4 + 3 =

3 + 4 =

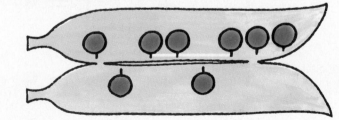

6 + 2 =

2 + 6 =

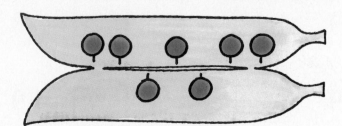

5 + 2 =

2 + 5 =

Nine coconuts

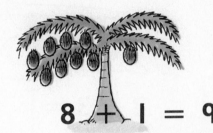

$8 + 1 = 9$

$\boxed{} + \boxed{} = 9$

Use counters.

$\boxed{} + \boxed{} = 9$ $\boxed{} + \boxed{} = 9$

$\boxed{} + \boxed{} = 9$ $\boxed{} + \boxed{} = 9$

$\boxed{} + \boxed{} = 9$ $\boxed{} + \boxed{} = 9$

$\boxed{} + \boxed{} = 9$ $\boxed{} + \boxed{} = 9$

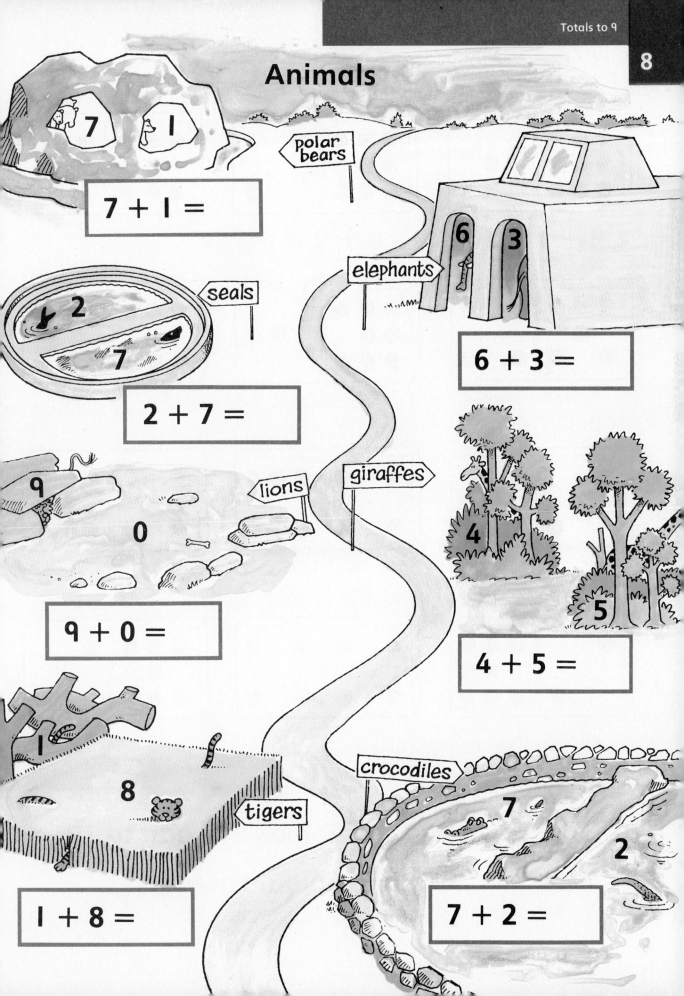

Animals

7   1

polar bears

7 + 1 =

6   3

elephants

6 + 3 =

seals

2

7

2 + 7 =

9

0

lions

giraffes

4

5

9 + 0 =

4 + 5 =

1

8

tigers

crocodiles

7

2

1 + 8 =

7 + 2 =

Add the spots.

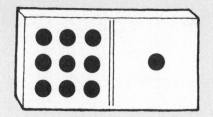

9 + 1 = 10

8 + 2 =

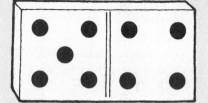

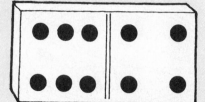

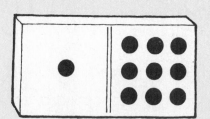

Some  add to 10.
Colour them .

Add

Some add to 10.   Colour them .

7 + 3	3 + 5	9 + 1	1 + 8
5 + 4	6 + 4	2 + 5	5 + 5
1 + 9	4 + 4	3 + 7	2 + 6
5 + 2	2 + 8	4 + 3	8 + 2

Find my name.

Colour if it adds to 10.

$1 + 9 =$ $3 + 6 =$ $5 + 4 =$

$6 + 3 =$

$2 + 7 =$ $7 + 3 =$

$6 + 2 =$

$2 + 8 =$ $5 + 5 =$ $4 + 6 =$

R 13

Plants

Make each 2p more.

6p

4p ✗   6p ✗   7p   5p   8p

Make each 3p more.

3p

6p

6p

5p   7p   4p

Tickets

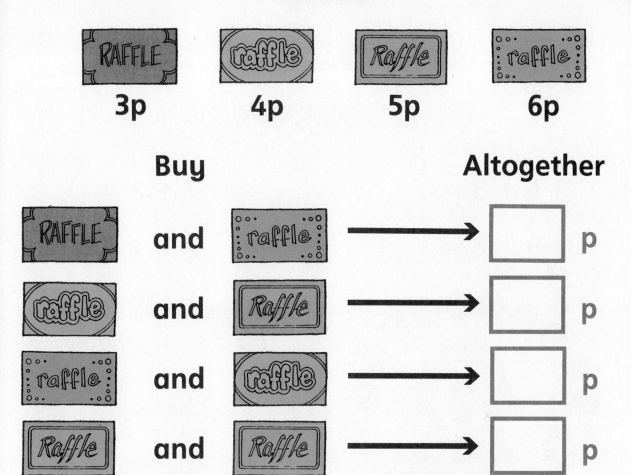

RAFFLE **3p**   raffle **4p**   Raffle **5p**   raffle **6p**

Buy   ## Altogether

RAFFLE **and** raffle → ☐ p

raffle **and** Raffle → ☐ p

raffle **and** raffle → ☐ p

Raffle **and** Raffle → ☐ p

Find the lucky numbers.

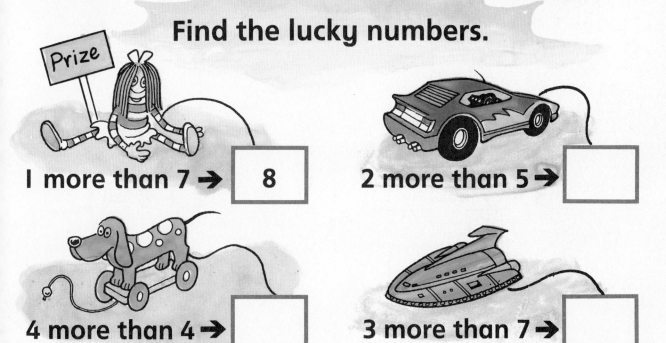

I more than 7 → **8**   2 more than 5 → ☐

4 more than 4 → ☐   3 more than 7 → ☐

Clowns

$5 + 4 =$ ☐

$4 + 5 =$ ☐

$6 + 3 =$ ☐

$3 + 6 =$ ☐

$7 + 2 =$ ☐

$2 + 7 =$ ☐

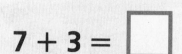

$6 + 4 =$ ☐

$4 + 6 =$ ☐

$7 + 3 =$ ☐

$3 + 7 =$ ☐

$8 + 1 =$ ☐

$1 + 8 =$ ☐

$8 + 2 =$ ☐

$2 + 8 =$ ☐

$9 + 1 =$ ☐

$1 + 9 =$ ☐

It's magic

$$2 + 3 + 1 =$$

$$3 + 4 + 2 =$$

$$5 + 2 + 2 =$$

$$4 + 1 + 3 =$$

$$\underline{} + \underline{} + \underline{} =$$

$$\underline{} + \underline{} + \underline{} =$$

$$0 + 5 + 5 = \square$$

$$3 + 5 + 0 = \square$$

$$2 + 1 + 6 = \square$$

$$1 + 4 + 5 = \square$$

Games

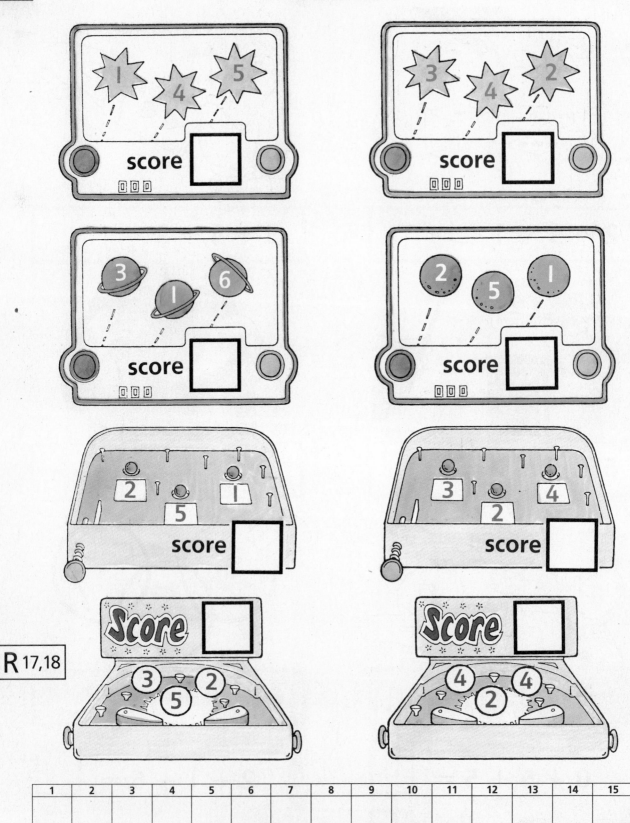

1	2	3	4	5	6	7	8	9	10	11	12	13	14	15

R 17,18

Published by Heinemann Educational Publishers, Halley Court, Jordan Hill, Oxford OX2 8EJ,
a division of Reed Educational and Professional Publishers Ltd.
ISBN 0 435 03707 2 © Scottish Primary Mathematics Group 1991.
First published 1991. Revised edition 1995.   97 98 99   7 6 5 4 3
Typeset and Illustrated by Oxprint Design. Printed by Jarrold Printing, Norwich.

ISBN 0-435-03088-4